HILAIRE BELLOC

THE BAD CHILD'S BOOK OF BEASTS
and MORE BEASTS FOR WORSE CHILDREN
and A MORAL ALPHABET

With Pictures by B. T. B.

DOVER PUBLICATIONS, INC.
NEW YORK

This new Dover edition, first published in 1961, is an unabridged and—except for new pagination—an unaltered republication of the following:

The Bad Child's Book of Beasts, first published by Duckworth and Company, London, in 1897.

More Beasts for Worse Children, first published by Duckworth and Company, London, in 1898.

A Moral Alphabet, first published by Edward Arnold, London, in 1899.

Standard Book Number: 486-20749-8

Library of Congress Catalog Card Number: 61-2226

Manufactured in the United States of America
Dover Publications, Inc.
180 Varick Street
New York 14, N. Y.

CONTENTS

Page

THE BAD CHILD'S BOOK OF BEASTS   1

Introduction 5
The Yak 9
The Polar Bear 15
The Lion 16
The Tiger 17
The Dromedary 18
The Whale 19
The Camel 24
The Hippopotamus 25
The Dodo 27
The Marmozet 31
The Camelopard 32
The Learned Fish 36
The Elephant 37
The Big Baboon 39
The Rhinoceros 43
The Frog 45

MORE BEASTS FOR WORSE CHILDREN   49

Introduction 53
The Python 59
The Welsh Mutton 64
The Porcupine 65
The Scorpion 68

The Crocodile 69
The Vulture 77
The Bison 79
The Viper 82
The Llama 86
The Chamois 90
The Frozen Mammoth 91
The Microbe 95
A MORAL ALPHABET 97

THE

BAD CHILD'S
BOOK OF
BEASTS.

Verses by
H. BELLOC.

Pictures by
B. T. B.

Child! do not throw this book about;
    Refrain from the unholy pleasure
Of cutting all the pictures out!
    Preserve it as your chiefest treasure.

Child, have you never heard it said
    That you are heir to all the ages?
Why, then, your hands were never made
    To tear these beautiful thick pages!

Your little hands were made to take
    The better things and leave the worse ones:
They also may be used to shake
    The Massive Paws of Elder Persons.

And when your prayers complete the day,
    Darling, your little tiny hands
Were also made, I think, to pray
    For men that lose their fairylands.

DEDICATION.

---·---

To Master EVELYN BELL
Of Oxford.

Evelyn Bell,

I love you well.

INTRODUCTION.

I call you bad, my little child,
 Upon the title page,
Because a manner rude and wild
 Is common at your age.

The Moral of this priceless work
 (If rightly understood)
Will make you—from a little Turk—
Unnaturally good.

5

Do not as evil children do,

　Who on the slightest grounds

Will imitate

the Kangaroo,

　With wild unmeaning bounds.

Do not as children badly bred,
  Who eat like little Hogs,
And when they have to go to bed
  Will whine like Puppy Dogs:

Who take their manners from the Ape,
  Their habits from the Bear,
Indulge the loud unseemly jape,
  And never brush their hair.

But so control your actions that
Your friends may all repeat,

'This child is dainty as the Cat,
And as the Owl discreet.'

The Yak.

As a friend to the children

commend me the Yak.

You will find it exactly the thing:

It will carry and fetch,

you can ride on its back,

Or lead it about

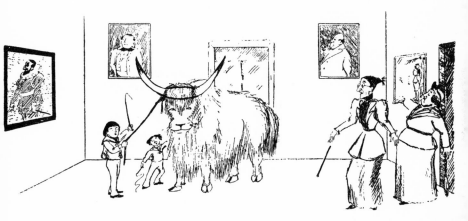

with a string.

The Tartar who dwells on the plains of Thibet

(A desolate region of snow)

Has for centuries made it a nursery pet,

And surely the Tartar should know!

Then tell your papa where the Yak can be got,

And if he is awfully rich

He will buy you the creature—

or else

he will *not.*

(I cannot be positive which.)

The Polar Bear.

The Polar Bear is unaware

Of cold that cuts me through:
For why? He has a coat of hair.
I wish I had one too!

The Lion.

The Lion, the Lion, he dwells in the waste,

He has a big head and a very small waist;

But his shoulders are stark, and his jaws they are
  grim,

And a good little child will not play with him.

The Tiger.

The Tiger, on the other hand,

is kittenish and mild,
He makes a pretty playfellow for any little child;
And mothers of large families (who claim to common sense)

Will find a Tiger well repay the trouble and expense.

The Dromedary.

The Dromedary is a cheerful bird :

I cannot say the same about the Kurd

The Whale.

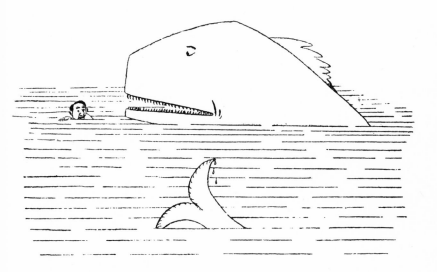

The Whale that wanders round the Pole

Is not

a table fish.
You cannot bake or boil him whole,
Nor serve him in a dish ;

But you may cut his blubber up
And melt it down for oil,

And so replace

the colza bean
(A product of the soil).

These facts should all be noted down
   And ruminated on,

By every boy in Oxford town
   Who wants to be a Don.

The Camel.

"The Ship of the Desert."

The Hippopotamus.

I shoot the Hippopotamus

with bullets made of platinum,

Because if I use leaden ones

his hide is sure to flatten 'em.

The Dodo.

The Dodo used

to walk around,

And take the sun and air.

The Sun yet warms his native ground—

The Dodo is not there!

The voice which used to squawk and squeak

Is now for ever dumb—

Yet may you see his bones and beak

All in the Mu-se-um.

The Marmozet.

The species Man and Marmozet
Are intimately linked;

The Marmozet survives as yet,
But Men are all extinct.

The Camelopard.

The Camelopard, it is said
  By travellers (who never lie),

He cannot stretch out straight in bed
    Because he is so high.
The clouds surround his lofty head,
    His hornlets touch the sky.

How shall
    I hunt
      I
this quadruped?
cannot tell!
Not I!

(A picture of how people try
And fail to hit that head so high.)

I'll buy a little parachute
(A common parachute with wings),
I'll fill it full of arrowroot
And other necessary things,

And I will slay this fearful brute
With stones and sticks and guns and slings.

(A picture of

how people shoot
With comfort from a parachute.)

The Learned Fish.

This learned Fish has not sufficient brains
To go into the water when it rains.

The Elephant.

When people call this beast to mind,

They marvel more and more

At such a

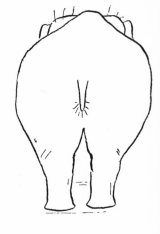

LITTLE tail behind,

So *LARGE* a trunk before.

The Big Baboon.

The Big Baboon is found upon
  The plains of Cariboo;

He goes about

with nothing on
(A shocking thing to do.)

But if he

dressed respectably
And let his whiskers grow,

How like this Big Baboon would be

To Mister So-and-so!

The Rhinoceros.

Rhinoceros, your hide looks all undone,

You do not take my fancy in the least:

You have a horn where other brutes have none :

Rhinoceros, you are an ugly beast.

The Frog.

Be kind and tender to the Frog,

And do not call him names,
As ' Slimy skin,' or ' Polly-wog,'
    Or likewise ' Ugly James,'
Or ' Gape-a-grin,' or ' Toad-gone-wrong,'
    Or ' Billy Bandy-knees' :

The Frog is justly sensitive
    To epithets like these.

No animal will more repay
  A treatment kind and fair ;
At least

so lonely people say
Who keep a Frog (and, by the way,
  They are extremely rare).

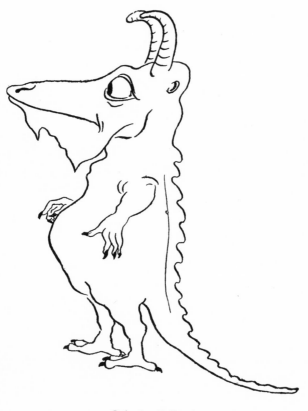

Oh! My!

DEDICATION.

To

Miss ALICE WOLCOTT BRINLEY,

Of Philadelphia.

52

MORE BEASTS

FOR WORSE CHILDREN

INTRODUCTION

THE parents of the learned child
    (His father and his mother)
Were utterly aghast to note
The facts he would at random quote
On creatures curious, rare and wild;
    And wondering, asked each other:

"An idle little child like this,
How is it that he knows
What years of close analysis
Are powerless to disclose?

Our brains are trained, our books are big,
And yet we always fail

To answer why the Guinea-pig
Is born without a tail.

Or why the Wanderoo* should rant
In wild, unmeaning rhymes,

* Sometimes called the " Lion-tailed or tufted Baboon of Ceylon."

Whereas the Indian Elephant
Will only read *The Times*.

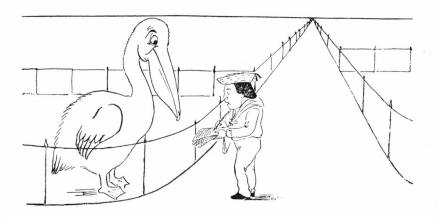

Perhaps he found a way to slip
  Unnoticed to the Zoo,
And gave the Pachyderm a tip,
  Or pumped the Wanderoo.

Or even by an artful plan
  Deceived our watchful eyes,
And interviewed the Pelican,
  Who is extremely wise."

"Oh ! no," said he, in humble tone,
   With shy but conscious look,
"Such facts I never could have known
   But for this little book."

The Python

A PYTHON I should not advise,—
It needs a doctor for its eyes,
And has the measles yearly.

However, if you feel inclined
To get one (to improve your mind,
And not from fashion merely),
Allow no music near its cage ;

And when it flies into a rage
Chastise it, most severely.

I had an aunt in Yucatan
Who bought a Python from a man
        And kept it for a pet.
She died, because she never knew
These simple little rules and few;—

The Snake is living yet.

The Welsh Mutton

The Cambrian Welsh or Mountain Sheep
      Is of the Ovine race,
His conversation is not deep,
      But then—observe his face!

The Porcupine

What! would you slap the Porcupine?
Unhappy child—desist!
Alas! that any friend of mine
Should turn Tupto-philist.*

* From τύπτω = I strike; φιλέω-ᾶ = I love; one that loves to strike. The word is not found in classical Greek, nor does it occur among the writers of the Renaissance—nor anywhere else.

To strike the meanest and the least
Of creatures is a sin,

How much more bad to beat a beast
With prickles on its skin.

The Scorpion

The Scorpion is as black as soot,
    He dearly loves to bite;
He is a most unpleasant brute
    To find in bed, at night.

The Crocodile

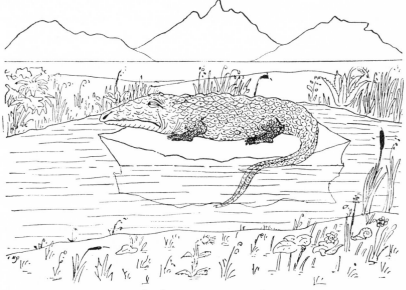

Whatever our faults, we can always engage
That no fancy or fable shall sully our page,
So take note of what follows, I beg.
This creature so grand and august in its age,
In its youth is hatched out of an egg.

And oft in some far Coptic town
The Missionary sits him down
    To breakfast by the Nile:
The heart beneath his priestly gown
    Is innocent of guile;

When suddenly the rigid frown
Of Panic is observed to drown
    His customary smile.

Why does he start and leap amain,

And scour the sandy Libyan plain

Like one that wants to catch a train,

Or wrestles with internal pain ?

Because he finds his egg contain—
Green, Hungry, horrible and plain—
An Infant Crocodile.

The Vulture

The Vulture eats between his meals,
And that's the reason why

He very, very rarely feels
    As well as you and I.

His eye is dull, his head is bald,
    His neck is growing thinner.
Oh! what a lesson for us all
    To only eat at dinner!

The Bison

The Bison is vain, and (I write it with pain)
The Door-mat you see on his head

Is not, as some learned professors maintain,
The opulent growth of a genius' brain;

But is sewn on with needle and thread.

The Viper

Yet another great truth I record in my verse,
That some Vipers are venomous, some the reverse;
    A fact you may prove if you try,

By procuring two Vipers, and letting them bite;

With the *first* you are only the worse for a fright,

But after the *second* you die.

The Llama

The Llama is a woolly sort of fleecy hairy goat,
With an indolent expression and an undulating throat
     Like an unsuccessful literary man.

And I know the place he lives in (or at least—I think I do)
It is Ecuador, Brazil or Chili—possibly Peru;
    You must find it in the Atlas if you can.

The Llama of the Pampasses you never should confound
(In spite of a deceptive similarity of sound)
  With the Lhama who is Lord of Turkestan.

For the former is a beautiful and valuable beast,
But the latter is not lovable nor useful in the least ;
And the Ruminant is preferable surely to the Priest
Who battens on the woful superstitions of the East,
  The Mongol of the Monastery of Shan.

The Chamois

The Chamois inhabits
Lucerne, where his habits
   (Though why I have not an idea-r)
Give him sudden short spasms
On the brink of deep chasms,
   And he lives in perpetual fear.

The Frozen Mammoth

This Creature, though rare, is still found to the East
Of the Northern Siberian Zone.

It is known to the whole of that primitive group
That the carcass will furnish an excellent soup,
　　　Though the cooking it offers one drawback at least
　　　　(Of a serious nature I own):

If the skin be *but punctured* before it is boiled,
Your confection is wholly and utterly spoiled.

And hence (on account of the size of the beast)
The dainty is nearly unknown.

The Microbe

The Microbe is so very small
You cannot make him out at all,
But many sanguine people hope
To see him through a microscope.
His jointed tongue that lies beneath
A hundred curious rows of teeth;
His seven tufted tails with lots
Of lovely pink and purple spots,

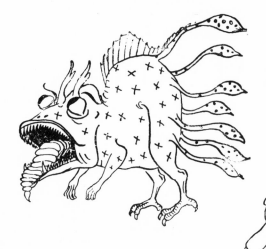

On each of which a pattern stands,
Composed of forty separate bands;
His eyebrows of a tender green;
All these have never yet been seen—
But Scientists, who ought to know,
Assure us that they must be so. . . .
Oh! let us never, never doubt
What nobody is sure about!

A

MORAL ALPHABET

IN WORDS OF FROM ONE TO SEVEN SYLLABLES

BY

H. B.

WITH ILLUSTRATIONS BY

B. B.

DEDICATION.

**TO THE GENTLEMAN
ON PAGE 143**

stands for

Archibald who told no lies,
And got this lovely volume for a prize.

The Upper School had combed and oiled their hair,
And all the Parents of the Boys were there.
In words that ring like thunder through the Hall,
Draw tears from some and loud applause from all, —

The Pedagogue, with Pardonable Joy,
Bestows the Gift upon the Radiant Boy :—

" Accept the Noblest Work produced as yet "
(Says he) " upon the English Alphabet ;
" Next term I shall examine you, to find
" If you have read it thoroughly.   So mind !"

And while the Boys and Parents cheered so loud,
That out of doors

a large and anxious crowd
Had gathered and was blocking up the street,
The admirable child resumed his seat.

Moral.

Learn from this justly irritating Youth,
To brush your Hair and Teeth and tell the Truth.

B stands for Bear.

When Bears are seen
Approaching in the distance,

Make up your mind at once between
Retreat and Armed Resistance.

A Gentleman remained to fight—
With what result for him ?

The Bear, with ill-concealed delight,
Devoured him, Limb by Limb.

Another Person turned and ran ;
    He ran extremely hard :
The Bear was faster than the **Man**,
    And beat him by a yard.

MORAL.

Decisive action in the hour of need
Denotes the Hero, but does not succeed.

C stands for Cobra ; when the Cobra

bites

An Indian Judge, the Judge spends restless nights.

Moral.

This creature, though disgusting and appalling,
Conveys no kind of Moral worth recalling.

D

The Dreadful

Dinotherium he
Will have to do his best for D.
The early world observed with awe
His back, indented like a saw.
His look was gay, his voice was strong ;
His tail was neither short nor long ;
His trunk, or elongated nose,
Was not so large as some suppose ;
His teeth, as all the world allows,
Were graminivorous, like a cow's.

He therefore should have wished to pass
Long peaceful nights upon the Grass,
But being mad the brute preferred
To roost in branches, like a bird.*
A creature heavier than a whale,
You see at once, could hardly fail
To suffer badly when he slid

* We have good reason to suppose
  He did so, from his claw-like toes.

And tumbled

                (as he always did).
His fossil, therefore, comes to light
All broken up : and serve him right.

                MORAL.

If you were born to walk the ground,
Remain there ; do not fool around.

E

stands for

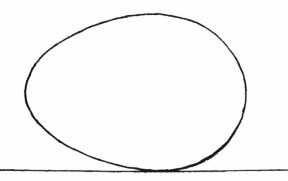

Egg.

MORAL.

The Moral of this verse
Is applicable to the Young.   Be terse.

F

for a

Family taking a walk
In Arcadia Terrace, no doubt :
The parents indulge in intelligent talk,
While the children they gambol about.

At a quarter-past six they return to their tea,
Of a kind that would hardly be tempting to me,
  Though my appetite passes belief.
There is Jam, Ginger Beer, Buttered Toast, Marmalade,
With a Cold Leg of Mutton and Warm Lemonade,
And a large Pigeon Pie very skilfully made
  To consist almost wholly of Beef.

MORAL.

A Respectable Family taking the air
  Is a subject on which I could dwell ;
It contains all the morals that ever there were,
  And it sets an example as well.

G

stands for Gnu, whose weapons of Defence
Are long, sharp, curling Horns, and Common-sense.
To these he adds a Name so short and strong,

An Uitlander.

That even Hardy Boers pronounce it wrong.

How often on a bright Autumnal day
The Pious people of Pretoria say,
"Come, let us hunt the——" Then no more is heard
But Sounds of Strong Men struggling with a word.
Meanwhile, the distant Gnu with grateful eyes
Observes his opportunity, and flies.

MORAL.

Child, if you have a rummy kind of name,
Remember to be thankful for the same.

H was a

Horseman who rode to the meet,
And talked of the Pads of the fox as his " feet "—
An error which furnished subscribers with grounds
For refusing to make him a Master of Hounds.

He gave way thereupon to so fearful a rage,
That he sold up his Stable and went on the Stage,
And had all the success that a man could desire
In creating the Part of

"The Old English Squire."

MORAL.

In the Learned Professions, a person should know
The advantage of having two strings to his bow.

I

the Poor Indian, justly called " The Poor,"

He has to eat his Dinner off the floor.

MORAL.

The Moral these delightful lines afford
Is : " Living cheaply is its own reward '

J

stands for James, who thought it immaterial
To pay his taxes, Local or Imperial.
In vain the Mother wept, the Wife implored,
James only yawned as though a trifle bored.

The Tax Collector called again, but he
Was met with Persiflage and Repartee.

When James was hauled before the learned Judge,
Who lectured him, he loudly whispered, " Fudge ! "
The Judge was startled from his usual calm,
He

struck the desk before him with his palm,
And roared in tones to make the boldest quail,
"*J stands for James*, IT ALSO STANDS FOR JAIL."

And therefore, on a dark and dreadful day,
Policemen came and took him all away.

MORAL.

The fate of James is typical, and shows
    How little mercy people can expect
Who will not pay their taxes ; (saving those
    To which they conscientiously object.)

K

for the Klondyke, a Country of Gold,
Where the winters are often excessively cold;
Where the lawn every morning is covered with rime,
And skating continues for years at a time.
Do you think that a Climate can conquer the grit
Of the Sons of the West?   Not a bit !   Not a bit !

When the weather looks nippy, the bold Pioneers
Put on two pairs of Stockings and cover their ears,
And roam through the drear Hyperborean dales
With a vast apparatus of Buckets and Pails;

Or wander through wild Hyperborean glades
With Hoes, Hammers, Pickaxes, Matlocks and Spades.

There are some who give rise to exuberant mirth
By turning up nothing but bushels of earth,
While those who have little cause excellent fun
By attempting to pilfer from those who have none.
At times the reward they will get for their pains
Is to strike very tempting auriferous veins ;
Or, a shaft being sunk for some miles in the ground,
Not infrequently nuggets of value are found.
They bring us the gold when their labours are ended,
And we—after thanking them prettily—spend it.

MORAL.

Just you work for Humanity, never you mind
If Humanity seems to have left you behind.

L

was a Lady, Advancing in Age,
Who drove in her carriage and six,
With a Couple of Footmen a Coachman and Page,
Who were all of them regular bricks.

If the Coach ran away, or was smashed by a Dray,
Or got into collisions and blocks,
The Page, with a courtesy rare for his years,
Would leap to the ground with inspiriting cheers,
While the Footman allayed her legitimate fears,
And the Coachman sat tight on his box.

At night as they met round an excellent meal,
   They would take it in turn to observe :
" What a Lady indeed ! . . what a presence to feel ! . ."
   " What a Woman to worship and serve ! . . ."

But, perhaps, the most poignant of all their delights
   Was to stand in a rapturous Dream
When she spoke to them kindly on Saturday Nights,
   And said " They deserved her Esteem."

MORAL.

Now observe the Reward of these dutiful lives :
    At the end of their Loyal Career
They each had a Lodge at the end of the drives,
    And she left them a Hundred a Year.
Remember from this to be properly vexed
    When the newspaper editors say,
That "The type of society shown in the Text
    " Is rapidly passing away."

M

was a Millionaire who sat at Table,
And ate like this—

as long as he was able ;
At half-past twelve the waiters turned him out :
He lived impoverished and died of gout.

Moral.

Disgusting exhibition !   Have a care
When, later on you are a Millionaire,
To rise from table feeling you could still
Take something more, and not be really ill.

stands for Ned, Maria's younger brother,

Who, walking one way, chose to gaze the other.

In Blandford Square—a crowded part of town—
Two People on a tandem knocked him down ;
Whereat

a Motor Car, with warning shout,
Ran right on top and turned him inside out :
The damages that he obtained from these
Maintained him all his life in cultured ease.

MORAL.

The law protects you.   Go your gentle way :
The Other Man has always got to Pay.

O

stands for Oxford.   Hail ! salubrious seat
Of learning ! Academical Retreat !
Home of my Middle Age ! Malarial Spot
Which People call Medeeval (though it's not).
The marshes in the neighbourhood can vie
With Cambridge, but the town itself is dry,
And serves to make a kind of Fold or Pen

Wherein to herd a lot of Learned Men.

Were I to write but half of what they know,
It would exhaust the space reserved for " O " ;
And, as my book must not be over big,
I turn at once to " P," which stands for Pig.

MORAL.

Be taught by this to speak with moderation
Of places where, with decent application,
One gets a good, sound, middle-class education.

P

stands for Pig, as I remarked before,

A second cousin to the Huge Wild Boar.
But Pigs are civilized, while Huge Wild Boars

Live savagely, at random, out of doors,
And, in their coarse contempt for dainty foods,
Subsist on Truffles, which they find in woods.
Not so the cultivated Pig, who feels
The need of several courses at his meals,
But wrongly thinks it does not matter whether

He takes them one by one

or all together.
Hence, Pigs devour, from lack of self-respect,
What Epicures would certainly reject.

MORAL.

Learn from the Pig to take whatever Fate
Or Elder Persons heap upon your plate.

Q

for Quinine, which children take

With Jam and little bits of cake.

MORAL.

How idiotic !   Can Quinine
Replace Cold Baths and Sound Hygiene ?

R

the Reviewer,

reviewing my book,
At which he had barely intended to look ;

But the very first lines upon " A " were enough
To convince him the *Verses* were excellent stuff.
So he wrote, without stopping, for several days
In terms of extreme, but well-merited Praise.
To quote but one Passage : " No Person " (says he),
" Will be really content without purchasing three,
" While a Parent will send for a dozen or more,
" And strew them about on the Nursery Floor.
" The Versification might call for some strictures
" Were it not for its singular wit ; while the Pictures,
" Tho' the handling of line is a little defective,
" Make up amply in *verve* what they lack in perspective."

MORAL.

The habit of constantly telling the Truth
Will lend an additional lustre to Youth.

S

stands for Snail, who, though he be the least,
Is not an uninstructive Hornèd Beast.

His eyes are on his Horns, and when you shout
Or tickle them, the Horns go in and out.
Had Providence seen proper to endow
The furious Unicorn or sober Cow
With such a gift the one would never now
Appear so commonplace on Coats of Arms.
And what a fortune for our failing farms
If circus managers, with wealth untold,
Would take the Cows for half their weight in gold !

MORAL.

Learn from the Snail to take reproof with patience,
And not put out your Horns on all occasions.

T

for the Genial Tourist, who resides
In Peckham, where he writes Italian Guides.

MORAL.

Learn from this information not to cavil
At slight mistakes in books on foreign travel.

U

for the Upas Tree,

that casts a blight
On those that pull their sisters' hair, and fight.

But oh ! the Good !   They wander undismayed,
And (as the Subtle Artist has portrayed)
Dispend the golden hours at play beneath its shade.*

MORAL.

Dear Reader, if you chance to catch a sight
Of Upas Trees, betake yourself to flight.

---

* A friend of mine, a Botanist, believes
   That Good can even browse upon its leaves.
   I doubt it. . . .

V for

the unobtrusive Volunteer,
Who fills the Armies of the World with fear.

MORAL.
Seek with the Volunteer to put aside
The empty Pomp of Military Pride.

My little victim, let me trouble you
To fix your active mind on W.

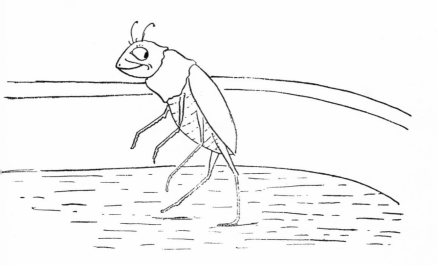

The WATERBEETLE here shall teach
A sermon far beyond your reach :
He flabbergasts the Human Race
By gliding on the water's face
With ease, celerity, and grace ;
But if he ever stopped to think
Of how he did it, he would sink.

MORAL.

Don't ask Questions !

X

No reasonable little Child expects
A Grown-up Man to make a rhyme on X.

MORAL.

These verses teach a clever child to find
Excuse for doing all that he's inclined.

Y

stands for Youth (it would have stood for Yak,
But that I wrote about him two years back).
Youth is the pleasant springtime of our days,
As Dante so mellifluously says
(Who always speaks of Youth with proper praise).
You have not got to Youth, but when you do
You'll find what He and I have said is true.

MORAL.

Youth's excellence should teach the Modern Wit
First to be Young, and then to boast of it.

Z

for this Zébu, who (like all Zebús)*
Is held divine by scrupulous Hindoos.

MORAL.

Idolatry, as you are well aware,
Is highly reprehensible.   But there,
We needn't bother,—when we get to Z
Our interest in the Alphabet is dead.

* **Von** Kettner writes it " *Zébu* "; Wurst " *Zebu* ":
  I split the difference and use the two.